JUNGLE JA
IN SPAIN

GINA LARRY MIKEY ELLA ZIGGY

Authors: Louise & Noam Lederman
Illustrator: Jason James

First published in 2017 by Jungle Jam Publishing
www.jungle-jam.com

A CIP catalogue record for this book is available from the British Library.
ISBN 978-1-910762-08-0

We would like to thank everyone who has supported us on our Jungle Jam journey.
Thanks to our family and friends for believing in us and helping us to fulfil our dream.
Special thanks to our partners the Lim family - Charles, Priscila, Anjila, Theron and Valenciano.

JUNGLE JAM
IN SPAIN

WRITTEN BY
LOUISE & NOAM LEDERMAN
ILLUSTRATED BY JASON JAMES

Jungle Jam Publishing

Deep in the jungle amongst the swaying trees,
the music of the Jungle Jam band echoes in the breeze.

Their tour bus is ready, waiting just down the lane,
to take them on a musical adventure to Spain.

They jump off the bus in a bustling square,
so busy and colourful, friendly animals everywhere.

"Welcome to Spain and the city of Seville.
The music here is simply unreal."

"I am Dani the Donkey, so pleased to meet your band.
We have a busy schedule and a fantastic show planned."

The Jungle Jam band listen to Dani explain
all about the wonderful people of Spain.

But Ziggy the Zebra has other plans.
He wants to explore and meet his fans.

"This is the famous Alhambra Palace, so big and bold.
Bright orange bricks shining in silver and gold."

"There is beautiful art and so much to see.
You will learn about our culture and history."

Here is Ziggy, having lots of fun,
signing autographs in the sun.

Next they go to a flamenco club to see Dani dance.
The band can't wait to see her move and prance.

Dani says, "Flamenco is the sound of Spain, our special musical style.
The singing, dancing and snapping beats will surely make you smile."

The club is so cool, the band are super excited.
Dani appears on stage and they are all so delighted.

Here is Ziggy, eating tapas, the local food.
Lots of tiny dishes, it tastes so good!

They go for a long walk after the show.
Mikey loved Dani's dancing and wants to know...

"How did you make that beautiful sound?
Can you teach us while we walk around?"

Larry and Mikey give the castanets a try.
The snapping sound floats off into the sky.

"Where is Ziggy, that cheeky fella?
Let's try and find him," say Gina and Ella.

Here is Ziggy doing his own thing again.
How many times will he go missing in Spain?

Dani the Donkey and the Jungle Jam band
prepare for a photo shoot, don't they look grand?

Mikey tries a flamenco shirt in yellow and red.
Larry wears a waistcoat with a streak of gold thread.

Ella has a Spanish scarf and waves a fan in the air.
Gina is looking in the mirror, putting flowers in her hair.

"Where is Ziggy? Has he gone to play?
We really need him in the photos today."

Here is Ziggy having a rest.
Short naps are simply the best.

It's the final practice and Ziggy is here.
The band see him arrive and they all cheer.

But Ziggy's guitar sounds really bad.
He gets it wrong and it makes him sad.

Everyone is ready, but Ziggy's not happy at all.
He missed the photo shoot and his clothes are too small.

"Come on Ziggy, it will be fine.
We are here for you all the time."

Ziggy stopped to think about it for a moment...

I missed out on many things during this Spanish tour, forgot about my commitment to the band for sure.

Now I realise how important it is to be a good friend.

We are an awesome band and our friendship will never end.

Alhambra Palace

Flamenco Club

Stomp! Clap! Snap!

Photo Shoot

The Jungle Jam band learned so much in Spain. "Gracias!" they shout. "We will come back again."

ACTIVITY: SNAKES AND LADDERS

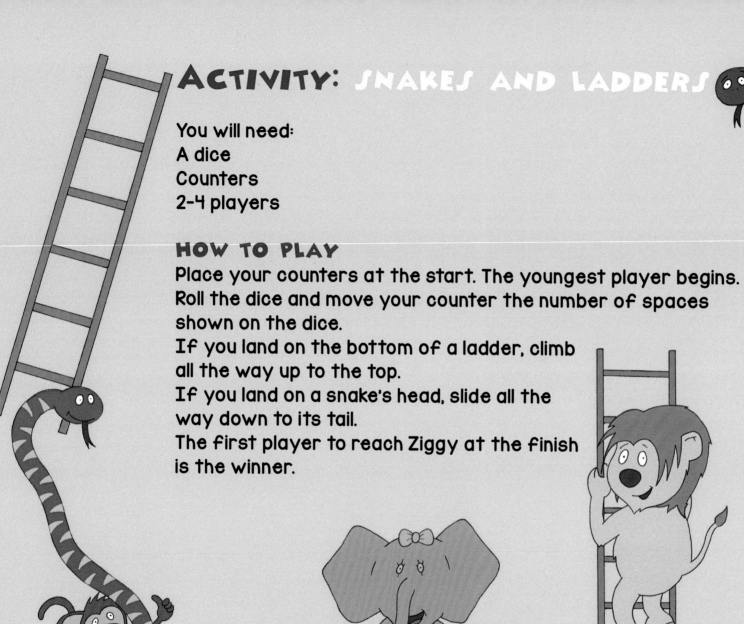

You will need:
A dice
Counters
2-4 players

HOW TO PLAY

Place your counters at the start. The youngest player begins.
Roll the dice and move your counter the number of spaces
shown on the dice.
If you land on the bottom of a ladder, climb
all the way up to the top.
If you land on a snake's head, slide all the
way down to its tail.
The first player to reach Ziggy at the finish
is the winner.

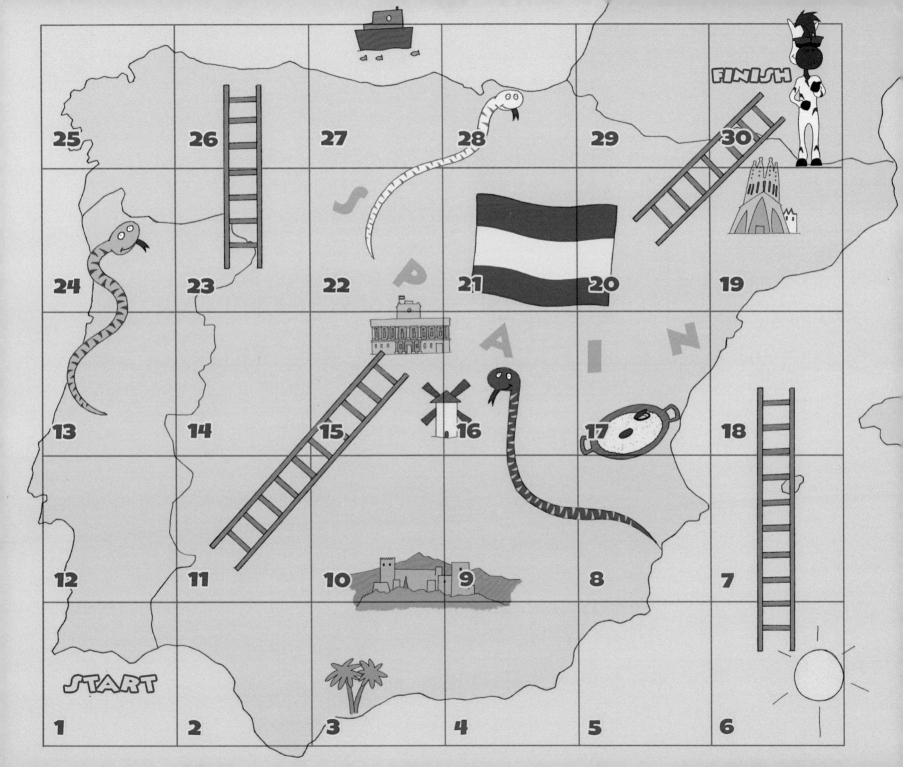

SPAIN FACTS

- **Spain** the largest country in Southern Europe

- **Seville** the largest city in Southern Spain where flamenco originated

- **Flamenco** a style of entertainment with song, music and dance

- **Alhambra** a large palace built in the 13th century in the city of Granada

- **Castanets** a wooden instrument used in flamenco music

- **Tapas** a variety of small dishes in Spanish cuisine

- **Gracias** [grah-si-as] 'thank you' in Spanish